CONTENTS

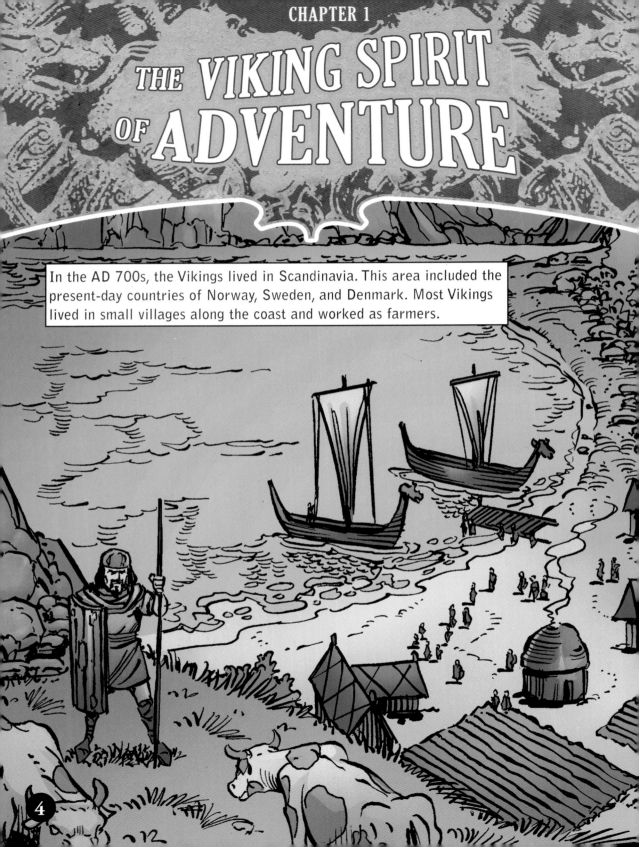

CHAPTER 1

THE VIKING SPIRIT OF ADVENTURE

In the AD 700s, the Vikings lived in Scandinavia. This area included the present-day countries of Norway, Sweden, and Denmark. Most Vikings lived in small villages along the coast and worked as farmers.

The Vikings used rivers and waterways called fjords to travel from village to village. They built strong, fast ships and became excellent seafarers and navigators.

Good farmland was hard to find in Scandinavia. Some Vikings began raiding other lands for riches.

In 793, Vikings landed in England and raided the Lindisfarne monastery.

Search the church! Look for jewels and gold!

Where are you taking me?! Let me go!

You're a slave now! Get on board!

By 850, many Vikings had decided to settle down in England.

We've thought of a better way to get rich.

We won't attack you if you pay us.

We'll pay you anything you want. Just don't hurt us!

The Vikings took over small villages and farmlands in England. The city of York became a large Viking town.

We were never able to own this much land back home.

Here our children will live better lives.

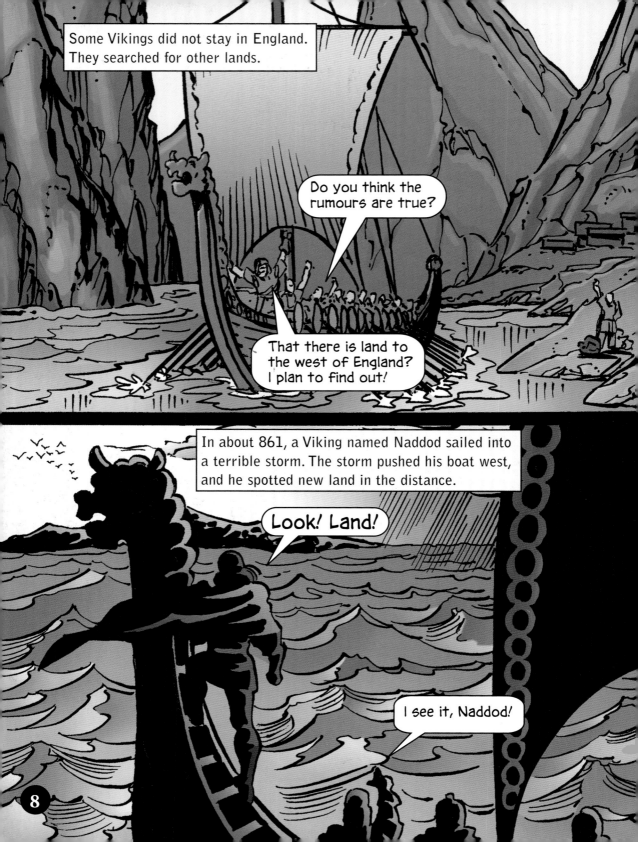

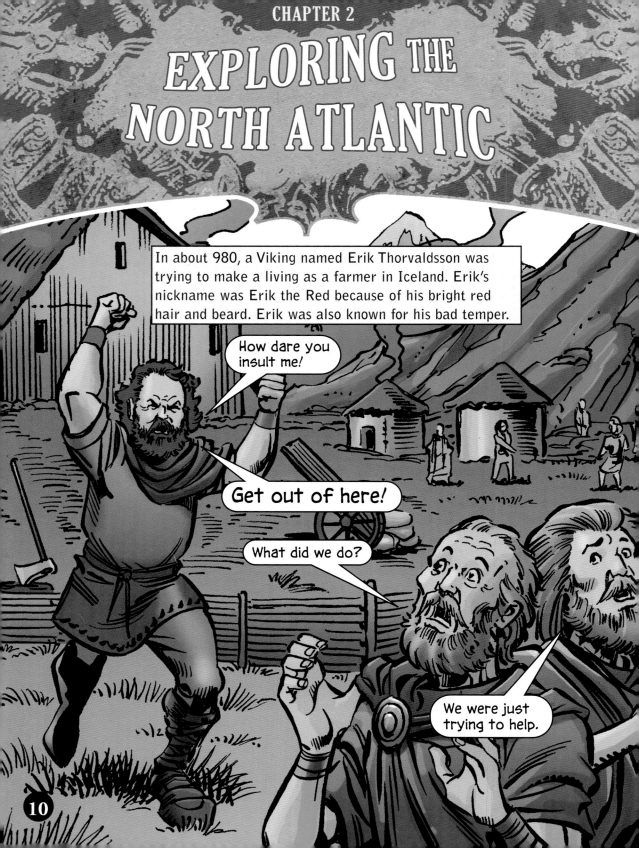

The same year Erik settled Greenland, a Viking named Bjarni Harjolfsson sailed to Iceland. He was looking for his family.

Bjarni, your family went to Greenland with Erik the Red.

Greenland?

How do I get there?

Sail west. Look for a land with fjords, green meadows, and distant mountains.

Bjarni set sail for Greenland. Three days into the voyage, he became lost in a thick fog. Bjarni's ship was blown off course.

When the fog lifted, Bjarni and his crew saw an unfamiliar land.

This doesn't look like the place we are looking for. There are thick forests here.

Let's go ashore and explore!

We don't have time. We must find Greenland.

CHAPTER 3

THE VIKINGS DISCOVER NORTH AMERICA

In 1000, Leif and his crew of 35 men sailed west from Greenland.

GREENLAND

HELLULAND
(BAFFIN ISLAND)

MARKLAND
(LABRADOR)

VINLAND
(NEWFOUNDLAND)

Sure enough, the Inuit returned in larger numbers and attacked the Vikings.

Thorvald's been hit by an arrow!

He's dead!

After the battle, the crew buried Thorvald near their camp. Then they loaded their ship with wood and grapes and sailed back to Greenland.

Soon after the battle, the Vikings decided they'd had enough. They packed up their belongings and left Vinland.

After Thorfinn left, very few Vikings ventured back to North America and none of them tried to settle down there.

The Viking settlements in Greenland eventually died out. In England, the Vikings married local people and adopted local customs. In Iceland, they continued to prosper. Today, many Icelanders are related to the Vikings who first settled there.

27

MORE ABOUT
THE VIKINGS

- Vikings are often shown wearing horned helmets, but in reality, their helmets did not have horns.

- Many Vikings had descriptive names, such as Harald Fair-Hair, Svein Forkbeard, and Harald Bluetooth.

- Three days of the week are named after Viking gods. Wednesday is named for the ruler of the gods, Odin. Thursday is named for the god of thunder, Thor. Friday is named after Freya, the goddess of love.

- Around 1500, the Viking settlements in Greenland died out. No one knows exactly why. The Vikings may have died of disease or used up all the natural resources.

- In the 1960s, archaeologists found the remains of a Viking settlement at L'Anse aux Meadows in Newfoundland, Canada. This site is the only known Viking settlement in North America.

The Vikings also travelled east to Russia and the Middle East. Along the way, they traded goods, weapons, and silver with the people they met. They used the silver to make jewellery. Both men and women wore silver rings, necklaces, and brooches.

Vikings travelled on land using horses, wagons, skis, and sledges. They even made ice skates out of animal bones.

The Vikings used a type of ship called a *drakkar* to raid other lands. This ships was also known as a "dragon ship" because of the dragon carved on its front. *Drakkars*, like all Viking ships, were built to travel fast.

The Vikings created the earliest form of parliamentary government in Europe. Known as the Althing, this outdoor meeting allowed free men to voice problems and discuss laws.

Glossary

banish send someone away from a place and order them not to return

colony area that has been settled by people from another country

fjord long, narrow inlet of ocean between high cliffs

Inuit native people of northern Canada, parts of Greenland, and Alaska

navigator person who uses maps, compasses, and the stars to guide a ship

Internet Sites

http://www.nmm.ac.uk/explore/sea-and-ships/facts/ships-and-seafarers/the-vikings

You can find out about different types of Viking ships on this website, as well as navigation and life on board the boats.

http:www.historyofyork.org.uk/themes/life-in-viking-york

This website tells you all about when the Vikings captured York.

http://www.bbc.co.uk/schools/vikings

On this website, you can find out about the daily lives of the Vikings, their beliefs, and their settlements.

READ MORE

History of Britain: The Saxons and Vikings, Jane Shuter
(Heinemann Library, 2007)

History Opens Windows: The Vikings, Jane Shuter
(Heinemann Library, 2008)

Men, Women, and Children: In Viking Times, Colin Hynson
(Wayland, 2009)

New Explore History: Romans, Anglo-Saxons, and Vikings in Britain (Heinemann Library, 2005)

BIBLIOGRAPHY

The Viking Saga, Peter Ludwig Brent (Weidenfeld and Nicolson, 1975)

A History of the Vikings, Gwyn Jones (Oxford University Press, 2001)

The Vikings, Else Roesdahl, translated by Susan M. Margeson and Kirsten Williams (Penguin, 1998)

The Oxford Illustrated History of the Vikings, P. H. Sawyer (Oxford University Press, 1997)

INDEX